DISC

DISNEY'S

TREASURE PLANET

DISCOVER

Disney's

Treasure Planet

PUFFIN BOOKS

ONTENTS

Captain Flint

AND THE

LEGEND OF Treasure Planet

A lizard-like, multi-eyed alien, Captain Nathaniel Flint was a cruel and notorious pirate who plundered ships, stealing precious treasures and Arcturian solar crystals, the most precious minerals in the galaxy.

But one day, Flint and his band of space pirates stumbled across an even greater treasure — a device that could open a portal to almost any other planet in the universe and transport them there instantly. With this device, Captain Flint and his army looted and pillaged a thousand worlds. Appearing from nowhere, they took what they wanted, then vanished without a trace.

1

Captain Flint and his band of pirates stashed their ill-gotten gains in the subterranean core of the planet-sized device, which later became known as Treasure Planet.

But as time passed, Captain Flint became more paranoid, fearing that his looted treasures would be taken from him. Afraid for their lives, his crew deserted Flint by escaping through the portal.

Determined to keep all the treasures to himself, just before he died, Flint set up an explosive device that would be triggered by anyone who tried to enter the core of the planet.

Welcome to Montressor

A once thriving but now poor and neglected mining community, Montressor is just one of more than a hundred planets in a huge empire. Mainly populated by migrant workers from surrounding planets, this remote space outpost is home to many different alien species, including the elephant-like Benbonians. Jim Hawkins and his mum are among the few humans living there.

Jim's parents migrated to the port of Benbow when he was a baby. Leland Hawkins had great ambitions for getting rich quick in the mines. However, this didn't work out and, unable to cope with the responsibilities of being a father, Leland left his wife and son while Jim was still a young boy.

Whilst growing up, Jim was forever getting into trouble, particularly for soaring across 'no-go' zones on his solar surfer. Made with a sail of solar-energy panels and an engine attached to a wooden skateboard-like body, Jim is able to perform the most fantastic stunts.

Ultimately, it is Jim's solar-surfing talent that saves the RLS *Legacy* and its crew when Treasure Planet is engulfed by a huge explosion. He hastily cobbles together a makeshift solar surfer and skilfully guides the ship through a portal, and safely back to Montressor's spaceport, Crescentia.

4

The Benbow Inn

The **Benbow Inn**, owned by Jim Hawkins's mother, is a quaint hostelry that caters to a bizarre mixture of alien guests. Rushing around to serve her customers with their usual orders of strange-looking food and drink, Sarah's main worry is her son, Jim – and what he is getting up to.

Benbow Inn Specials:

Kirellian jellyworms
(live, squirming worms)

Purp juice (extract of a purple-coloured, lemon-shaped piece of fruit, similar to an apple)

Bonzabeast stew
(a culinary delight often served during long journeys through space)

Yellato (a yellow vegetable that looks like a potato)

Families of cyclopses and frog-like aliens crowd into Sarah's hilltop inn for their meals. And if Sarah's not fast enough on her feet, amphibious children with wandering hands help themselves to food from other diners' plates!

Before long Jim comes home – with the 'help' of two Robo-Constables, who march him through the door! The police officers, who patrol Montressor, have once again impounded Jim's beloved solar surfer and arrested him for flying in a restricted area.

Doctor Doppler

The dog-like Doctor Delbert Doppler often pops into the Benbow Inn for a plateful of chowder and a chat with his friend, Sarah Hawkins. A shy and retiring bachelor, the doctor lives on a huge baroque estate with only his pet bullyadous for company. Alone in his observatory, surrounded by his star charts, books and telescope, the wealthy astronomer secretly yearns for some adventure in his rather dull life.

When he decides to chaperone Jim Hawkins in his search for Treasure Planet and the legendary 'loot of a thousand worlds', the kindly doctor finds more excitement and adventure than he bargained for! But Delbert Doppler shows true courage when the RLS *Legacy* ascends into the etherium. Bravely battling against a cosmic storm, the doctor helps to take on the crew of mutinous space sailors, eventually winning the heart of the ship's commander, Captain Amelia.

BULLYADOUS

Big and powerful, the bullyadous is an energetic, floppy-eared beast of burden, often used to pull hover-carriages on Montressor. As well as pulling Doctor Doppler's carriage, Delilah the bullyadous is also his pet.

efore making his escape from Treasure Planet, Captain Flint's young cabin boy, a turtle-like alien named **Billy Bones**, took the 'key' to the portals. Without the key, Flint was trapped on Treasure Planet forever.

BILLY BONES

More than a hundred years later, Billy Bones crashes his space ship into a dock near Jim Hawkins's home. The now old and wizened Bones has spent a lifetime trying to escape the clutches of an evil cyborg and his band of cut-throat pirates, who were after the contents of his precious treasure chest.

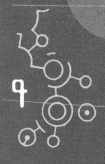

The Map!

Taking refuge inside the Benbow Inn, Bones takes a gold metallic sphere from his chest and gives it to Jim. The size of a tennis ball, the sphere has strange engravings on it. This is the 'map' used to activate the portal on Treasure Planet.

As Jim unlocks the device, a spark appears and then the sphere begins to glow. Then a 3D holographic image of planets and stars is projected from the sphere, filling the room. One of those planets is Treasure Planet!

SPACEPORT

Financing the expedition to Treasure Planet, Doctor Doppler's first job is to visit the spaceport in order to commission a ship and hire a captain and crew for the voyage.

The crescent-shaped space station is always bustling with activity. Humans, aliens and spaceships of every size, shape and colour are constantly moving about the busy port. Huge merchant ships, space galleons, longboats and ferries drift in and out, transporting cargo and passengers to destinations throughout the galaxy.

Disembarking from a space ferry, Jim and Doctor Doppler search for their ship along the dock. They soon find the **RLS** *Legacy* – secured by an astral anchor, an invisible force field used to anchor ships at bay on spaceports. A majestic and gleaming three-masted solar galleon, the ship's sails are made of a fabric derived from solar crystals.

Solar crystals, the most valuable mineral in the galaxy, are used to create solar energy, which is the major source of power. Frequently stolen by pirates from ships during transportation, these crystals are worth nearly as much as gold.

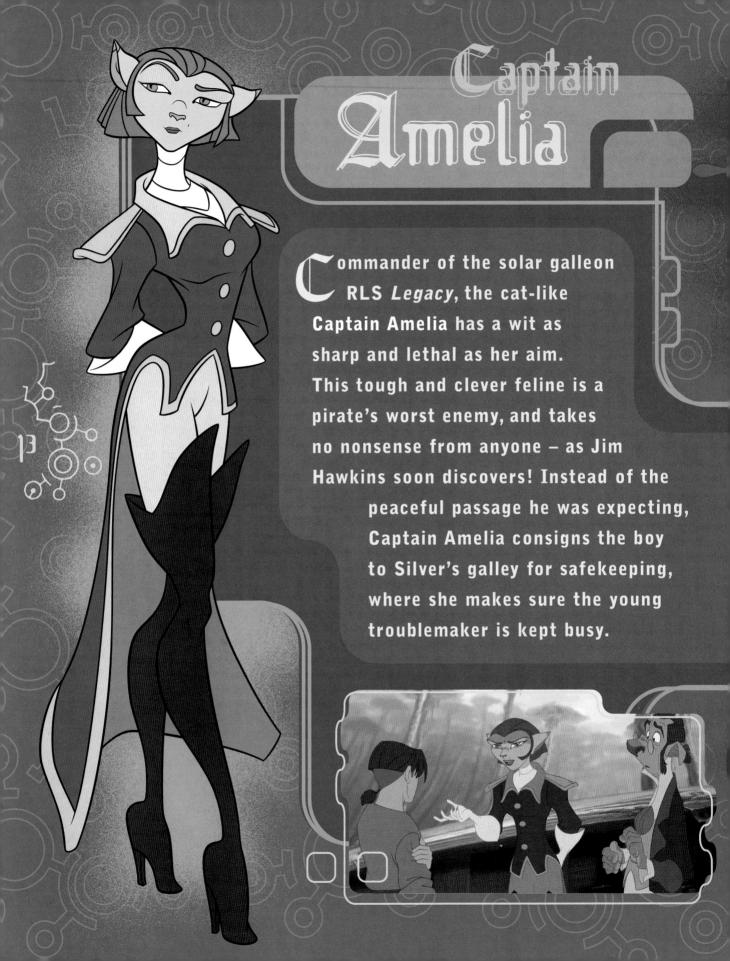

Captain Amelia

Commander of the solar galleon
RLS *Legacy*, the cat-like
Captain Amelia has a wit as
sharp and lethal as her aim.
This tough and clever feline is a
pirate's worst enemy, and takes
no nonsense from anyone – as Jim
Hawkins soon discovers! Instead of the
peaceful passage he was expecting,
Captain Amelia consigns the boy
to Silver's galley for safekeeping,
where she makes sure the young
troublemaker is kept busy.

13

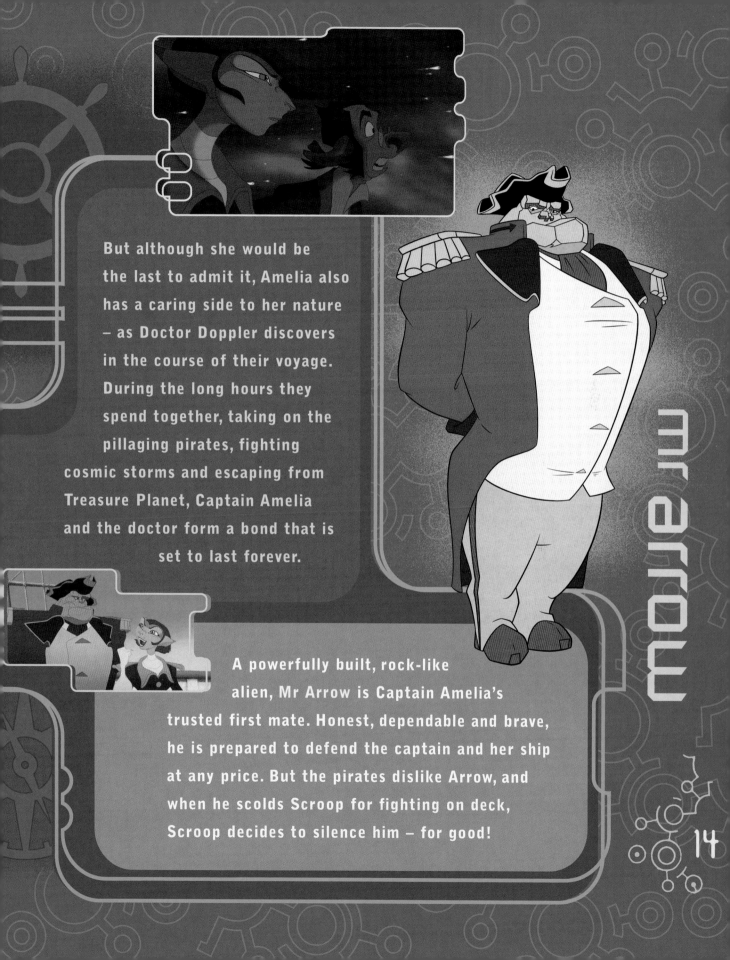

But although she would be the last to admit it, Amelia also has a caring side to her nature – as Doctor Doppler discovers in the course of their voyage. During the long hours they spend together, taking on the pillaging pirates, fighting cosmic storms and escaping from Treasure Planet, Captain Amelia and the doctor form a bond that is set to last forever.

A powerfully built, rock-like alien, Mr Arrow is Captain Amelia's trusted first mate. Honest, dependable and brave, he is prepared to defend the captain and her ship at any price. But the pirates dislike Arrow, and when he scolds Scroop for fighting on deck, Scroop decides to silence him – for good!

Mr Arrow

SILVER

John Silver is a cyborg. Part man and part machine, his right side is made up of metal gears, ratchets and flywheels, which he uses with great dexterity! He is fun-loving and kind, but beneath the wit and charm lurks a ruthless obsession. He will do anything to claim the legendary loot hidden on Treasure Planet. In fact, serving as ship's cook aboard RLS *Legacy* is only a cover for this pillaging pirate ...

Beware the CYBORG

MORPH

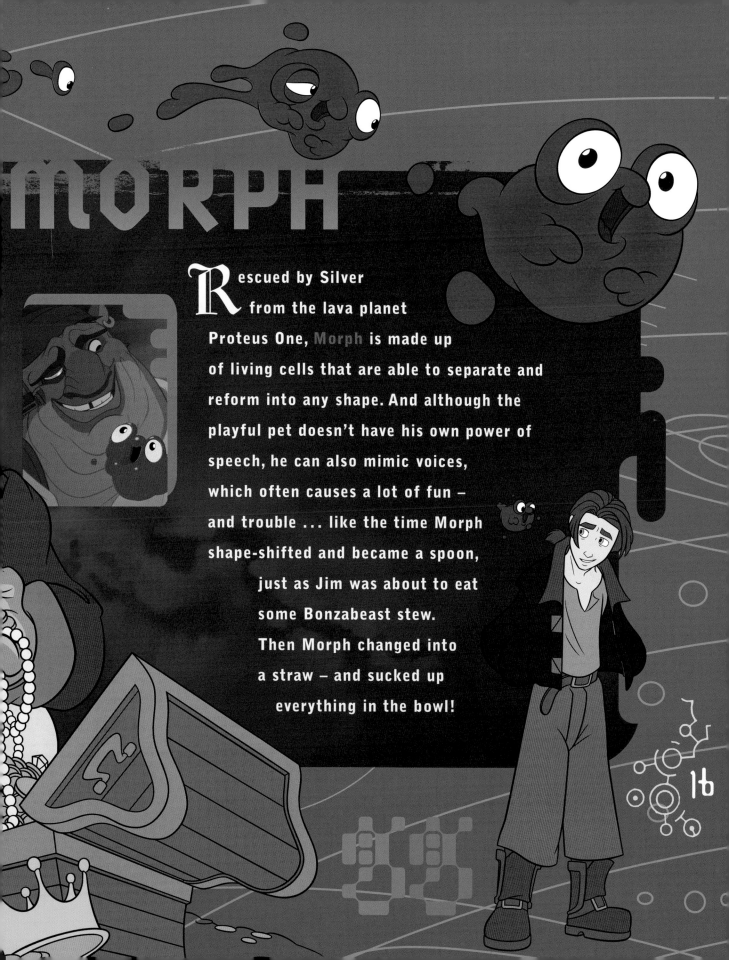

Rescued by Silver from the lava planet Proteus One, Morph is made up of living cells that are able to separate and reform into any shape. And although the playful pet doesn't have his own power of speech, he can also mimic voices, which often causes a lot of fun – and trouble ... like the time Morph shape-shifted and became a spoon, just as Jim was about to eat some Bonzabeast stew. Then Morph changed into a straw – and sucked up everything in the bowl!

Pillaging Pirates

Although they come from very different, distant planets throughout the universe, Silver's pirates all have one interest in common – to find the lost loot of a thousand worlds! Acting as ship's crew aboard the RLS *Legacy*, they go about their work, waiting and listening for any information that will lead them to Flint's treasure trove.

Scroop, a sinister spider-like alien with a major attitude problem, is the ruthless ringleader. Resenting Silver's authority and despising Jim Hawkins on sight, he is the ultimate in evil and treachery. Scroop lurks in the darkest shadows, speaking in a spine-chilling hiss that is capable of curdling cream. It is Scroop who slashes Arrow's lifeline with his lethal claw, sending him spinning into the centre of a black hole, never to be seen again.

Scroop

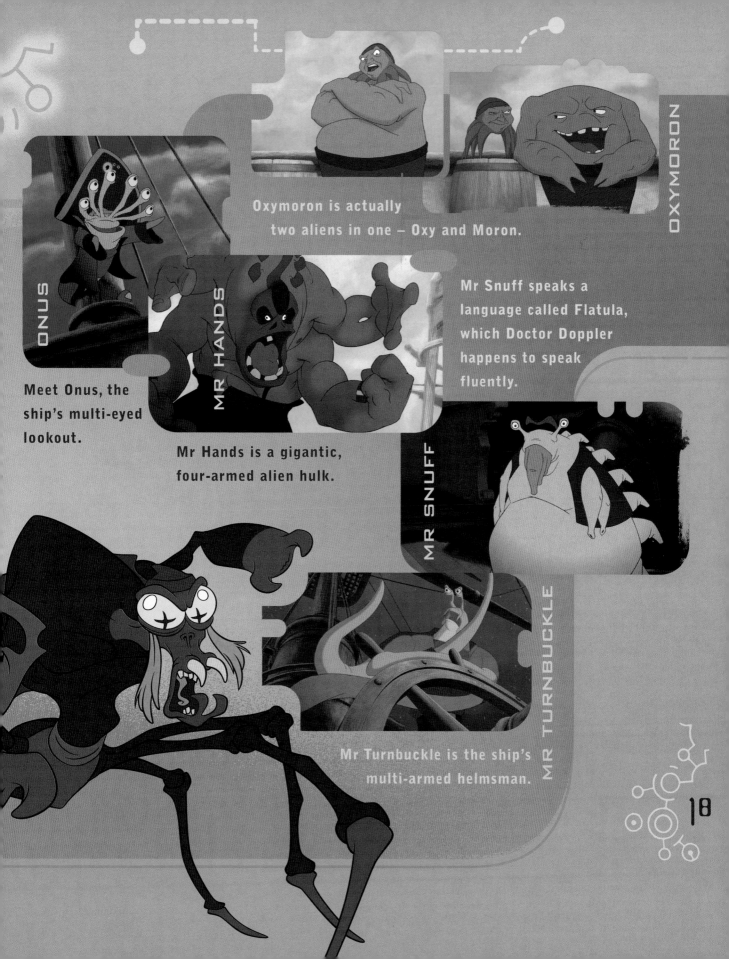

OXYMORON

Oxymoron is actually two aliens in one — Oxy and Moron.

ONUS

Meet Onus, the ship's multi-eyed lookout.

MR HANDS

Mr Hands is a gigantic, four-armed alien hulk.

Mr Snuff speaks a language called Flatula, which Doctor Doppler happens to speak fluently.

MR SNUFF

MR TURNBUCKLE

Mr Turnbuckle is the ship's multi-armed helmsman.

The Etherium

To get from one planet to another, solar-powered ships travel through the etherium, the atmosphere-filled outer space in the universe of Treasure Planet.

As the RLS *Legacy* ascends into the etherium, huge, whale-like Orcus Galactici glide through the atmosphere, shooting massive spouts of nebula spray. Mantabirds fly past the ship, in a similar fashion to seagulls flying over the sea.

Rattle the Stars

This is a world where vessels soar through space, encountering all kinds of dangers. The crew of the RLS *Legacy* is in big trouble when the ship is hit by a cosmic storm. Without warning, the ageing star Pellicid explodes, sending solar particles and deadly star shards raining down.

SUPERNOVA

A supernova is a huge explosion that occurs at the end of a star's life. It releases a huge amount of energy, expelling the outer layers of the star and becoming extremely bright. What remains is a neutron star or a black hole.

BLACK HOLE

A black hole is a massive object in space so dense that, within a certain area, its gravitational field does not let anything escape from it, not even light.

20

Gorbomite is a valuable mineral used to create artificial gravity. Without it, travellers would float away – and disappear into space, just like Mr Arrow does when Scroop cuts his lifeline.

ARTIFICIAL GRAVITY

As the **RLS** *Legacy* descends into the etherium, everyone floats up off the deck. Mr Snuff quickly engages artificial gravity by pulling a lever and, as an electro-magnetic gravity field washes over the deck, everyone drops back down with a bump!

When the red dwarf
star Pellucid turns
supernova, radiating
streams of energy,
solar particles and
deadly shards,
Captain Amelia gives
the order to change
course.

Jim, Silver and the rest of the
crew race to the mainmast and
tie lifelines around their
waists. The lifelines, secured
to a base at the foot of the mainmast,
are used to stop the crew from flying
off the deck during a storm.

As the supernova overtakes
the **RLS** *Legacy*, the ship
is suddenly engulfed in a
rain of fiery star shards,
which punctures one of
the solar sails. Scroop
and the other riggers
have to scramble quickly
up the rigging and
close the sails.

22

Mutiny on board the RLS Legacy

Without warning, **mutiny** erupts on board the RLS *Legacy*. Smashing down the armoury's locked door, the marauding pirates grab the weapons – and attack! Shooting tiny balls of laser energy at anything that moves, the pistol-like flintlocks prove to be powerful weapons.

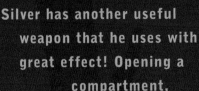

Silver has another useful weapon that he uses with great effect! Opening a compartment, Silver reveals his leg howitzer – a secret cyborg leg cannon. As Captain Amelia, Doppler and Jim race down a narrow gangway towards the ship's hangar bay, Silver fires his cannon to blast open the locked door between them.

But the scheming pirates aren't prepared for Captain Amelia's courage and determination. With Jim Hawkins and Doctor Doppler by her side, Captain Amelia gives orders to retaliate. Using flintlocks, they return fire and escape on to a longboat.

Fearing the longboat will get away, one of the pirates fires a laser cannon at it. A high-powered ball of explosive laser energy rips through the mainsail, breaking off the engine and injuring Amelia.

LONGBOATS

Longboats are small, fourteen-person exploration ships stowed on solar galleons.

One million years before Jim Hawkins was born, an advanced race of alien scientists, known as the **Forefathers**, built a planet-sized device which they used to create a portal that could instantly transport them to almost any other place in the universe. This device was later to become known as **Treasure Planet**, a luminescent, two-ringed, green planet somewhere in the galaxy.

Treasure Planet

The Forefathers used this device
for research, exploring different
worlds and gaining knowledge of
other civilizations, never causing harm to any of the
worlds they visited. Eventually, the Forefathers
evolved beyond physicality,
merged to become a brilliant
force of living energy and
drifted away. Their device then
lay dormant for centuries
... until Flint came along!

Covering the surface of Treasure Planet is a forest of giant
helium trees, tethered to boulders that float around. As Jim
and his friends discover when they land on the planet, these
helium trees have
a tendency to
explode on
contact – like
huge gas bags!

While searching Treasure Planet for a place to hide, Jim Hawkins meets B.E.N. A mechanical mess, it is difficult to believe that the robot was once a top-of-the-range Bio-Electronic Navigator.

b.e.n.

BIO-ELECTRONIC NAVIGATOR

Before he died, Captain Flint made sure **B.E.N.** could never reveal the whereabouts of his treasure by removing the robot's memory circuit. Marooned for a century, the lonely chatterbox tries to help Jim and his friends, but he just seems to make matters worse.

When Jim stumbles across the skeleton of Captain Flint, he finds B.E.N.'s missing memory circuit in the cunning pirate's clenched fist. With his missing chips now back in place, the robot starts to remember Flint's long-buried secrets...

28

The mutinous pirates pursue Captain Amelia and friends and surround their hideout. Silver wastes no time in forcing Jim to unlock the spherical map and, as the map opens, living pixels swirl out. The tiny points of light form an image, guiding them across the terrain of Treasure Planet.

Unlocking the Map

Searching Treasure Planet for Flint's treasure, Jim, his friends and the pirates come across a sheer cliff. On the cliff's rock-face, hidden behind brambles, is a pattern made up of strange hieroglyphics, just like the ones on the map.

Inserting the map into an indentation he has found,
Jim and the others watch as the hieroglyphic pattern
lights up and lifts off the cliff, turning into a
spherical holographic control mechanism.

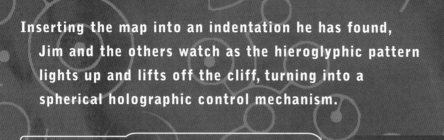

Just as Jim is about to touch the
controller, the ground starts
to rumble beneath his feet.
Beams of energy stream
across the landscape, coming
together at the base of the
cliff and finally shooting up
into the sky. In a brilliant
flash of light, a thirty-metre-
high triangle opens in the sky,
directly in front of the cliff.

Peering into the
triangle, Jim and
Silver see a vast,
beautiful etherium
with a spectacular
spiral nebula.

30

The Portal

Jim quickly discovers that by touching different points on the control mechanism, other places appear in the triangle. Sweeping his finger across the controller, Jim and Silver see a crystal landscape, Montressor spaceport and even a desert world that is halfway across the galaxy.

At last Jim understands how Flint did it! He had used the triangular-shaped portal to roam the universe stealing treasure wherever he went!

With a little help from B.E.N., it doesn't take Jim too long to work out what had happened to Flint's treasure. It had been buried in the centroid of the mechanism – and the whole of Treasure Planet was the mechanism!

As Jim touches a Treasure Planet icon on the controller, there is a brilliant flash of light and the triangle opens on to a dark chamber.

Pushing Jim to one side, Silver and his greedy band of pirates step through the portal, in search of the hidden treasure trove.

As Silver goes through the portal, his metal leg hits a narrow beam at the floor of the chamber, which sets off a rapid blinking light.

Going further into the chamber, Silver, Jim and the crew are suddenly bathed in a bright, golden glow. And as they soon discover, the golden light is coming from the mountains of treasure that fill the chamber – there are sparkling gems and crystals of every size, shape and colour, and beautiful paintings, golden goblets, statues and weaponry. At last Silver's all-consuming dream has come true: he has found Flint's lost loot of a thousand worlds!

Flint's Loot

OF A THOUSAND WORLDS

The treasure covers a gigantic sphere in the centre of the chamber – this is the 'centroid of the mechanism'. Enormous prongs fire energy beams to and from giant receptors on the centroid that keep the machine in place.

Finding Flint's ship nearby, Jim drags B.E.N. on board. But they find more than they bargain for. Sitting on an elegant jewelled throne, surrounded by some of his other treasures, is the skeleton of Captain Flint!

Just as explosions begin to erupt around them, B.E.N. suddenly remembers the booby trap that Flint had set. A giant prong breaks loose and crashes down to the base of the centroid, causing a series of receptacles to get knocked out of alignment. The energy beams cut through the surface of the centroid, creating huge cracks. Flint's trap works exactly to plan. The whole planet is set to explode!

The Destruction
OF TREASURE PLANET

The energy core of the centroid quickly evaporates, leaving treasure pouring through the gaping cracks. If there is any chance of escaping from this planet, there is no time to lose!

Barely making it out alive, Jim and Silver manage to burst back through the triangle just in time. As the RLS *Legacy* looms in front of them, Jim and Silver leap aboard. With exactly two minutes and thirty-four seconds until the whole planet destructs, things are getting pretty sticky!

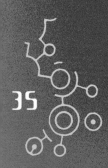

As huge portions of the planet's machinery explode around them, B.E.N. activates the thrusters – and the ship soars away from the triangle. It looks like the RLS *Legacy* has made it just in time ...

But a massive chunk of exploding debris crashes into the ship's mast, breaking it off. The damaged ship is never going to clear the exploding planet in time!

Jim zooms towards the controller on a knocked-together solar surfer that he and Silver have made. With only seconds to spare, he opens another portal for the RLS *Legacy* to zoom through just in time!

Return to Montressor

With one final big blast, Treasure Planet explodes behind the ship. As the RLS *Legacy* sails through the portal to a calm and tranquil etherium, Jim circles the vessel on his surfer, whooping and cheering. In the distance, the crescent-moon-shaped spaceport beckons. At last Jim and his friends – with the pirates, who are now safely constrained – head towards home.

Safely back in the spaceport, it's time for the pirates to pay the price for their dastardly deeds. But with the threat of imprisonment, Silver makes his escape down to the darkened hangar bay, where Jim finds him untying the mooring lines of the longboat.

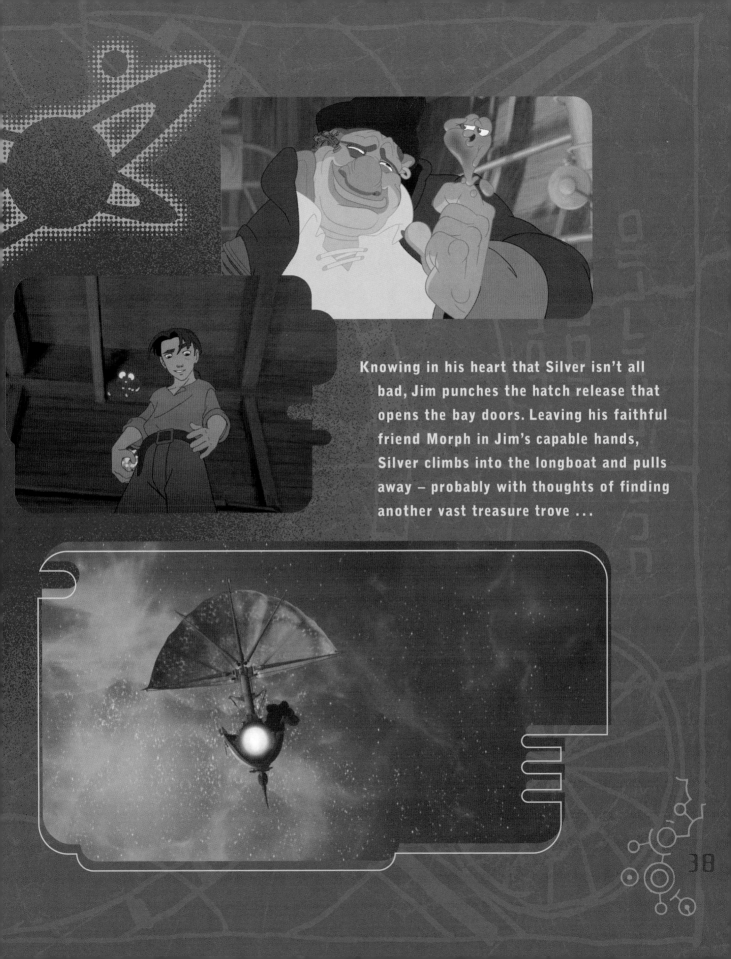

Knowing in his heart that Silver isn't all
bad, Jim punches the hatch release that
opens the bay doors. Leaving his faithful
friend Morph in Jim's capable hands,
Silver climbs into the longboat and pulls
away – probably with thoughts of finding
another vast treasure trove ...

Back at the Benbow Inn

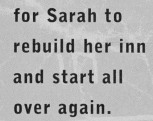

When pirates destroy the Benbow Inn, Sarah Hawkins thinks her days as an innkeeper are over. However, before he escapes from the *Legacy* in a longboat, Silver gives Jim a huge handful of jewels that he managed to stuff into his pockets before escaping from Treasure Planet. It is enough for Sarah to rebuild her inn and start all over again.

And this is where Doctor Doppler, Amelia and their children now often stop for a friendly chat and a bite to eat.

As B.E.N., now acting chef at the Benbow Inn, serves the busy throng of customers, Jim arrives with two Robo-Constables leading the way. But for once, Jim's not in any trouble. In fact, having joined the interstellar space academy, he has returned home for the holidays – to a warm reception and a proud mum!

And finally, we can't forget Morph, who has been left in Jim's safe care. When the shape-shifter's not babysitting the Doppler's children, he still causes mischief whenever he gets the opportunity – and you can bet that's pretty often!

Master Quiz

So you think you know all there is to know about Treasure Planet? Well, now you can put your knowledge to the test (and see if your memory is better than B.E.N.'s!) by answering these questions. All the answers appear somewhere in this book!

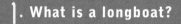

1. What is a longboat?

2. What are solar crystals used for?

3. What do the letters B.E.N. stand for?

4. What is a cyborg?

5. What is a bullyadous?

6. On which planet does Jim Hawkins live?

7. Who is the captain of the RLS *Legacy*?

8. What is Flint's first name?

9. What is the outer space in the universe of Treasure Planet called?

10. Who built Treasure Planet?

41

11. On which planet did Silver find Morph?

12. What are helium trees filled with?

13. What does a ship's crew tie round their waists to keep from flying off the deck?

14. Name the whale-like creatures that soar about the etherium.

15. What mineral is used to create artificial gravity?

16. Name the sinister, spider-like pirate serving on the RLS *Legacy*.

17. Who was Captain Flint's cabin boy?

18. What job does John Silver do aboard the RLS *Legacy*?

19. Name the inn owned by Jim Hawkins's mother.

20. Who financed Jim Hawkins's trip to Treasure Planet?

42

ANSWERS: 1. Small, fourteen-person exploration ship stowed on solar galleons; **2.** Energy; **3.** Bio-Electronic Navigator; **4.** Combination of part organ creature, part robot; **5.** Beast of burden; **6.** Montressor; **7.** Amelia; **8.** Nathaniel; **9.** Etherium; **10.** The Forefathers; **11.** Proteus One; **12.** Helium gas; **13.** Lifelines; **14.** Orcus Galactici; **15.** Gorbonite; **16.** Scroop; **17.** Billy Bones; **18.** Cook; **19.** Benbow Inn; **20.** Doctor Doppler.

PUFFIN BOOKS

Published by the Penguin Group
Penguin Books Ltd, 80 Strand, London WC2R ORL, England
Penguin Putnam Inc., 375 Hudson Street, New York, New York 10014, USA
Penguin Books Australia Ltd, 250 Camberwell Road, Camberwell, Victoria 3124, Australia
Penguin Books Canada Ltd, 10 Alcorn Avenue, Toronto, Ontario, Canada M4V 3B2
Penguin Books India (P) Ltd, 11 Community Centre, Panchsheel Park, New Delhi – 110 017, India
Penguin Books (NZ) Ltd, Cnr Rosedale and Airborne Roads, Albany, Auckland, New Zealand
Penguin Books (South Africa) (Pty) Ltd, 24 Sturdee Avenue, Rosebank 2196, South Africa

Penguin Books Ltd, Registered Offices: 80 Strand, London WC2R ORL, England
www.penguin.com

First published 2003
10 9 8 7 6 5 4 3 2

Set in Bell Gothic
Written by Lynne Gibbs
Designed by John Fordham

Printed in Italy by Printer Trento Srl

British Library Cataloguing in Publication Data
A CIP catalogue record for this book is available from the British Library

ISBN 0–141–31623–3